Danger! We ask the author a tricky question ...

Have you ever been involved in an accident?

When I was a little girl I lived near a farm. One very cold winter my older brother and I were walking on a pond in a farmer's field – something that was very dangerous to do! Suddenly, the ice gave way and my brother fell in. I managed to pull him out. We were both a bit worried about what our mum and dad would say when they found out. But luckily we didn't get into too much trouble.

For James, Caroline, Giles, Camilla and Bridget.

Dan and Lee were staying with Lee's gran, by the sea. One morning they went for a walk along the cliff path.

"See that?" said Lee. He pointed to a large rock jutting out over the sea. "That's called Dead Man's Rock."

"Why is it called that?" asked Dan.

"A long time ago, men and women were pushed off the rock to punish them for their crimes," Lee told him. "It's called Dead Man's Rock because they were all killed."

"Let's take a look," said Dan.

"Careful!" yelled Lee. "It's very
dangerous."

Dan looked over the edge. "It's a steep drop!" he said.

"Yes," said Lee. "I bet the men and women yelled *all* the way down as they fell."

"Gross!" said Dan.

Lee grinned. He pulled the old coin they had found in the woods out of his pocket. He tossed it in the air. The coin hummed and started to spin side-ways.

Lee made a grab for it, but he slipped and fell over the cliff. He landed with a thud on a small ledge half way down.

"Are you OK?" yelled Dan.

Lee began to moan. "No, I can't move my leg. I think it's broken."

"Stay still," shouted Dan. "I'm coming down."

Dan began to climb down the cliff, but it was too tricky.

"It's no good," he yelled. "I'll have to get help."

He ran to Lee's gran's house and told her what was up.

"I'll phone Sea Rescue," said Lee's gran.

Very soon, Sea Rescue and an air
ambulance arrived. The men pulled Lee to
safety with a very strong rope. They
checked him over. He *had* broken his leg.

"Thanks for helping me," Lee said to Dan.

"No big deal," said Dan. "But where is the coin?"

"It's here," said Lee. He opened his hand.

Dan looked at the coin and gasped.

"What's up?" asked Lee.

"It says **Danger**," said Dan.

Lee looked at the coin. "This coin is freaking me out," he said. He was shaking.

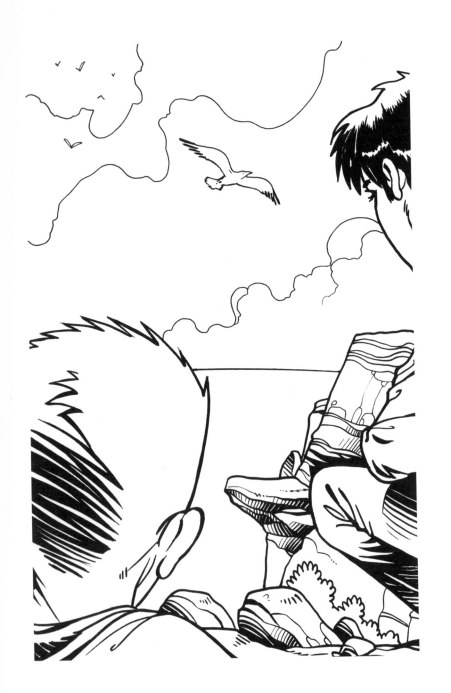

DARE OR DANGER

Like this book? Why not try the next one?

Dare You?

The coin says **Dare**.

Can Dan and Lee beat the bully?

For more info check out our website:
www.barringtonstoke.co.uk

DARE OR DANGER

Watch out for more **Dare or Danger** books coming soon ...

Up in Flames

The coin shows Danger.

There's a fire and someone's life is in danger ... can the boys come to the rescue?

Doom Ride

The coin shows Dare.

Lee and Dan dare to take on Doom Ride – the scariest ride in the theme park. But even they aren't prepared for what happens next ...

For more info check out our website:
www.barringtonstoke.co.uk